FOREST NATURE
CONSERVATION

GUIDELINES

LONDON : HMSO

ISBN 0 11 710292 X

Enquiries relating to this publication should be addressed to:
the Technical Publications Officer,
Forestry Commission,
Forest Research Station,
Alice Holt Lodge,
Wrecclesham,
Farnham,
Surrey
GU10 4LH

FOREST NATURE CONSERVATION GUIDELINES

Forests and woodlands are a rich and diverse habitat for wildlife, to be recognised and cared for by managers. The forest edge is a vivid frontier where the creatures of the woodland interact with those of the open moorland, green fields and wetlands. In the heart of the forest the trees and the open spaces have their own populations of flora and fauna.

Modern forestry practices have a 100-year history, yet it is only in the past 10 years that nature conservation has become a specific and essential part of the prescription. Backed by well-founded scientific research the forest manager's conservation plans are dovetailed with his programmes of timber production, landscape and recreational use of the land in his care.

These Guidelines, based on practical measures already being taken, will provide the manager with the advice he needs to reach high standards in 'state of the art' nature conservation in forestry throughout the country. They are a great step forward in the Forestry Commission's fulfilment of the duties placed upon it by the Wildlife and Countryside (Amendment) Act 1985 in both the management of its own land and in the exercise of its authority with private forestry.

Dr J. Morton Boyd
Forestry Commission Nature Conservation Consultant

FOREST NATURE CONSERVATION GUIDELINES

PURPOSE

The purpose of these guidelines is to give those engaged in forestry general but practical guidance on the maintenance and enhancement of the nature conservation value of existing woodlands and forests and on taking opportunities to develop nature conservation in new planting. It is important to stress that what is being managed is the totality of the woodland or forest area, and not merely the trees within it.

SCOPE AND USE OF THE GUIDELINES

Even in a country as small as Britain the range of woodland types and the consequent potential for nature conservation is very wide. Fortunately the range of knowledge is also extensive so that specialist advice will usually be available. These guidelines are intended to form a framework within which such local and specialist knowledge can be applied.

The Forestry Commission will observe these guidelines in its own operations and will expect to see them observed by private woodland owners and managers in proposals for work submitted for approval under all Forestry Commission grant schemes, or applications for felling permissions.

The management of woodland for nature conservation will seldom conflict with good landscape design as set out in the Forestry Commission's *Forest landscape design guidelines*. If so, the correct solution will be that which weights nature conservation and landscape according to the relative sensitivities of the particular sites.

FORESTRY COMMISSION STATUTORY RESPONSIBILITIES

The Forestry Act 1967 was amended by the Wildlife and Countryside (Amendment) Act 1985 so that the relevant section now reads:

"In discharging their functions under the Forestry Acts 1967 to 1979 the Commissioners shall, so far as may be consistent with the proper discharge of those functions, endeavour to achieve a reasonable balance between:

a. the development of afforestation, the management of forests and the production and supply of timber, and

b. the conservation and enhancement of natural beauty and the conservation of flora, fauna and geological or physiographical features of special interest."

Within the estate managed by the Forestry Commission the aims of nature conservation policy are:

– to identify and manage sites of special nature conservation interest;

– to enhance the nature conservation value of the estate as a whole;

– to promote public enjoyment of nature conservation where this is compatible with other conservation objectives.

CONSERVATION PLANS

There is no forest or woodland, large or small, which will not be better managed for nature conservation if intentions, prescriptions and achievements are recorded in a plan. The compilation of a plan is, of itself, a requirement to think clearly and act logically. It is also a desirable mechanism of communication, not only between owner and adviser but between successive managers. Plans need not be lengthy or complex – indeed the shorter and simpler the better. They are working reference documents to be developed continuously. The main purpose of such a plan is:

– to identify, describe and evaluate the present and potential conservation value of the woodlands or forest;

– to define conservation aims for sites of special interest and prescribe management regimes which will achieve the aims;

– to define how operations should proceed in relation to conservation aims in the wider woodland or forest;

– to develop a programme of conservation action.

The Forestry Commission has conservation plans covering every one of its Forest Districts and is ready to advise woodland and forest owners and managers on a useful format to adopt. In the Forestry Commission estate, such plans are not the exclusive preserve of forest managers but embrace engineers, land agents and others whose operations impinge upon the forest.

THE APPROACH TO NATURE CONSERVATION

● **Importance of the Entire Woodland or Forest**

All forests and woodlands, including their associated open ground, are of value for nature conservation. It is the responsibility of owners and managers to maintain and enhance that value. Although nature conservation will seldom have absolute priority outside special conservation sites, it must be accorded its place everywhere and be included in all planning and management. The cumulative wildlife benefit flowing from modest, well-founded adjustments to standard silvicultural operations can be very great.

● **Importance of Managing Habitats**

The key to good conservation practice is to maintain and add to the range of habitats.

- Give priority to maintaining and, where practicable, to extend existing habitats of conservation value.

- Aim to conserve and improve conditions for a whole community of plants and animals rather than for particular members and groups, unless urgent action is required to conserve rare, sensitive or endangered species.

- Aim for a balance of wooded and open habitats. Open ground is often more valuable than a change of tree species, both for nature conservation and for landscape purposes. In upland forests it may often be preferable to retain or create open ground habitat than to plant broadleaves.

- Develop a greater diversity of structure where wooded areas adjoin open ground, be it within or on the edge of the wood, so as to effect a gradual transition between them.

- Aim to get a mixture of stands of different ages throughout the woodland or forest. This automatically increases the quantity of the valuable edge habitat.

- Diversity is, however, not always a desirable goal. Forest and woodland diversity is naturally greater where soils are more fertile, the climate more favourable, towards the centre of the natural range of the woodland type, and in the later stages of ecological succession. Forests and woodlands comprising pioneer species, on infertile soils, and/or towards the altitudinal or latitudinal limits of their range are of conservation value because of the simplicity of species composition and, where extensive, because of the structure at a relatively large scale. Examples include the pine forests of East Anglia or those on littoral soils such as Culbin or Tentsmuir.

**Across Britain as a whole
the highest nature conservation value is assigned to forests and woodlands
which appear to be nearest their natural undisturbed state.** Since all have been
subjected to management to some extent over many hundreds of years, there
are no absolute models, but it is clear that high value can be attached to
woodland or forest consisting of native species, especially when the assemblage
of species appears close to that which probably occurred naturally. Such
species are host to a wealth of indigenous fauna and flora. Semi-natural
woodlands are more valuable if they are large enough to ensure the long-term
viability of the populations of the plants and animals within them. It is these
considerations which give value to such semi-natural systems as the Caledonian
pinewoods or the sessile oakwoods of the west coast of Britain.

The best examples of such woodlands have been declared by the Nature
Conservancy Council (NCC) as National Nature Reserves (NNR) and Sites of
Special Scientific Interest (SSSI). Plans for the management of SSSIs must be
agreed with the NCC and will be drawn up in consultation with that body.

Since each NNR and most SSSIs are being managed on the basis of a unique
plan, no more will be said of them here.

During the past few years the NCC has been compiling an Inventory of
Ancient Woodland Sites (AWS), distinguishing those which continue to carry
semi-natural woodland (ASNW). The compilation of the inventory has
enabled the Forestry Commission to frame guidelines on the basis of these
classifications. *Guidelines for the management of broadleaved woodland* and
Native pinewoods: grants and guidelines, published by the Forestry
Commission in 1985 and 1989 respectively, are essential reading for any
owners of these woodland types.

The first priority in conservation planning is therefore to identify semi-natural
forest and woodland and to prescribe a regime which will ensure its healthy
continuance. It will often be the case that the exclusion or restriction of
grazing animals, both wild and domestic, will be a prerequisite to the desirable
renewal of the woodland flora. The removal of trees or shrubs that are not
native to the area may also be an early requirement, especially if they are
threatening to suppress the native species.

Opportunities should be sought for extending such woodland by fencing-in adjacent open ground or sparsely stocked areas, and undertaking such silvicultural operations as are appropriate for securing regeneration. Natural regeneration is preferred but the practical difficulties and cost may rule this out.

A second priority is to consider the future of plantations on ancient woodland sites. Having been woodlands since early times, such sites may still retain ground flora and other species of particular conservation value. The aim of forest management should be to identify these features and to preserve and enhance them. Where nature conservation value is particularly high, these woodlands should be managed on the same lines as ancient semi-natural woodlands.

Where planting is carried out with nature conservation as a primary objective, the ideal is to use trees and shrubs which are native in the area. A detailed guide to the appropriate species, together with a specification for use compiled by the Nature Conservancy Council, is given in the Appendix.

Importance of Open Ground and Associated Edge Habitats

To a considerable extent the richness of wildlife within a woodland or forest will depend on the nature and distribution of this open ground and how it relates both to wooded areas and to land around the forest. Existing open ground will usually have arisen from a long series of management decisions which have had little or nothing to do with conservation. Managers should review and reorganise open ground so that it yields the maximum environmental dividends. Frequently this is the most rewarding conservation action that can be taken. The desirable proportion of open ground must vary from site to site but is likely to be least in the smallest woods. It would, however, be surprising if the total for any specific woodland or forest was less than 10 per cent or more than 20 per cent of the total area.

Land not bearing trees within a woodland or forest may include:

– roads, tracks, paths or other land set aside for access;

- service corridors, such as powerlines, public roads or railways;

- other land uses, such as farm holdings, radio masts or defence installations;

- land used for recreation, such as car parks, picnic areas, or playgrounds;

- areas deliberately kept open for operational purposes, such as timber stacking grounds or deer glades;

- areas where trees are sparse because of browsing, fire, windblow or other natural causes;

- water-bodies of all types and their banks;

- special conservation sites.

Where practicable open ground should be linked together within the woodland and with land beyond the forest to form interconnecting corridors along which wildlife can move. Together with wooded areas earmarked for long-term retention, this network will constitute the type of semi-permanent structure which is of such value in the New Forest or the Forest of Dean or the complex of pinewoods in upper Speyside. Open spaces required for day to day purposes, such as roads, can often be much enhanced by linking them in with other open space in this manner.

Transition zones between open and wooded ground are particularly valuable. They provide that structural diversity which is attractive to a wide range of woodland fauna, particularly invertebrates, and to the plant species which flourish in semi-woodland conditions.

As a rule, forest and woodland edges should be managed to benefit the whole community of plants and animals although where there are rare or endangered species it may be important to focus management on their specific needs. Widely different examples are nightingale, black grouse, and sand lizard. Seek specialist advice.

Active management of the edges of roads and rides is of benefit to wildlife. This can often be done inexpensively because there is easy access for mechanical treatment. This may involve periodic interventions to interrupt a natural succession towards woodland. Ideally, for conservation as well as engineering purposes, roads and rides should have a total width not less than the eventual tree height to avoid shading during the critical summer months. Those running east and west are likely to be of highest value for wildlife. North–south alignments and those on north-facing slopes must be wider to yield the same conservation benefits. Special action to favour wildlife may also include:

- retaining a grass-herb sward on either side by mowing in alternate years (where this is done there should be some bare or scraped areas to act as seed beds for low-growing plants which otherwise cannot compete with more vigorous vegetation, spring annuals often come into this category);

- on selected sites removing cut vegetation from the sward to promote the nutrient-deficient soil conditions favoured by certain plants;

- beyond this sward, encouraging the development of a low dense shrub zone by mechanical cutting on a rotation of 3 8 years;

- developing open glades at intersections of roads or rides;

- the use of herbicides to conservation ends.

Uncontrolled deer populations of all species can have a devastating effect on tree growth, on understorey and ground vegetation and on farm crops. In the absence of natural predators, control must be exercised by man. Deer management everywhere requires open areas where good browse species can develop, and where deer can be culled humanely and safely. Such deer glades must be identified or created early in a rotation and will usually be valuable for other conservation purposes. They can often be linked with the riparian zones required for the management of water. Excellent deer glades can be developed where flush vegetation is close to stands of native broadleaves.

It is advantageous when **all open land within the woodland or forest** is 'in hand'. Thus, it is important not to dispose of apparently unproductive pieces of open land, particularly in the heart of extensive forests. Should such land be under management unsympathetic to conservation, the wildlife in the surrounding woods may be in some jeopardy.

Within large upland forests **large open areas** may be utilised as seasonal grazings and can be rich in wildlife. Such areas should not be improved by reseeding or treated with inorganic fertiliser or pesticides. In these forests there will often be open ground above the trees but inside the forest fence because it has been deemed unplantable, or kept open for purposes of landscape design. Such areas of semi-natural vegetation will often have a higher conservation value because they have not been grazed for many years, especially if they contain a high percentage of dwarf shrub heath. Positive management may be required to produce a patchwork of different ages by controlled burning in the traditional manner, or by mechanical cutting.

The Value of Water

Detailed guidelines for the management of water within the forest are published by the Forestry Commission.

Watercourses are almost invariably rich in wildlife, especially the least accessible, and those with well developed pools. Riparian zones tend to be more sheltered and to have soils better than average for the locality, and so are often suitable for broadleaves and as deer pasture. They are important routes along which a range of wildlife can move and an essential part of the semi-permanent network of habitats. Watercourses are best managed by establishing protection zones along their length, within which substantial areas are kept open to sunlight, and by ensuring the development of thriving bankside vegetation. The essential features of good water management for nature conservation are as follows.

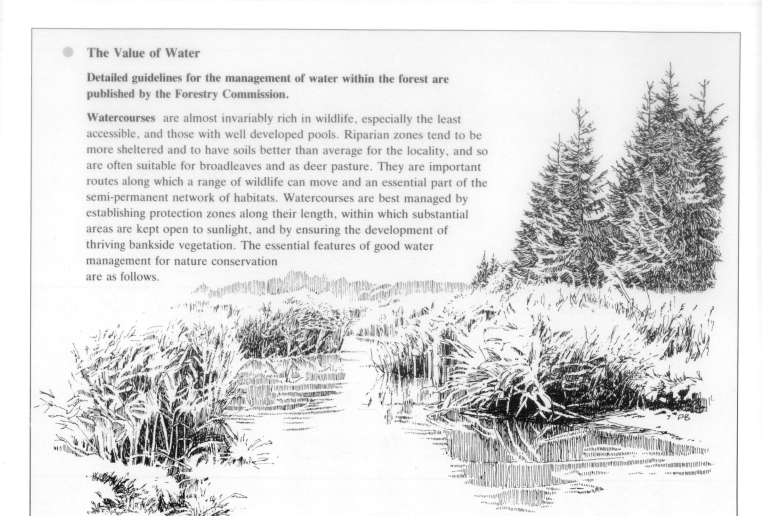

- Maintain at least half of a watercourse open to sunlight, with the remainder under intermittent shade from light-foliaged trees and shrubs. Periodic cutting may be required to maintain the appropriate proportions.

- Do not plant dense-foliaged trees any closer than 10 m from small headwater streams so that even when the branches are fully spread the stream will not be overgrown.

- Adjacent to larger streams and rivers, keep high forest trees far enough back to allow vigorous ground and shrub flora to develop in the zone and to allow sunlight to reach the stream when the trees are fully grown. Exceptions will exist when it is desired to encourage shade-loving plants such as ferns, mosses and liverworts or to provide habitat for otters. The width of these zones must be judged by studying the merits of the habitats present and what can be done to enhance them. The desired width will vary continuously.

- Plant light-foliaged broadleaves within the zone, using species native to the locality. Birch, willows, rowan, ash, hazel and aspen are often appropriate, depending on locality. Alder should be used with caution as it can cause excessive shading and there is some evidence that it can lead to acidification on certain infertile geologies.

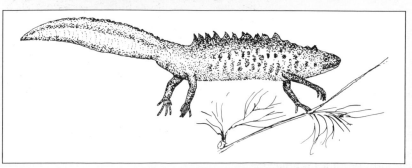

Water-bodies are of great value, particularly when they are shallow, rich in nutrients and in areas free from disturbance. Management of water-bodies should be on similar lines to that for watercourses, with heavily shading trees kept away from the water's edge but a scattering of light-foliaged trees and bushes in the protection zone. More attention is required to south-eastern, southern and south-western banks to ensure adequate light and sun, especially around small pools. Waterfowl must be able to see a water surface easily. Flight paths in various directions extending 50 m on average and up to 150 m in some directions may be required.

Water-bodies are obvious places for informal recreation and fishing. It is often desirable to keep some part of a water-body and its shoreline as a reserve for wildlife, especially when there are species present which will not tolerate disturbance. Restrict access and re-route footpaths if necessary. Think about hides as an alternative.

Small woodland pools are particularly valuable for amphibians in the agricultural lowlands where their numbers have been greatly reduced. Fish should not be introduced into pools used by amphibians. Fire dams dug when new forests were being established in the drier areas of Britain are now often of high conservation value. Their value (and safety) can often be enhanced by filling them to near the surface with large rounded stones. Gently sloping, shallow edges are most suitable for amphibians. In these drier areas road and rideside ditches may provide standing water which is rare elsewhere.

Wetlands vary from alder carr to wet grassland and peat mires with pool systems. Land use change has greatly reduced their extent, particularly in the lowlands. They are important ecologically and should not be planted. Their management requires care and knowledge.

– Many wetlands are somewhat unstable ecologically, drying out naturally as vegetation accumulates and natural succession moves towards woodland. Take expert advice before attempting to arrest or reverse the succession.

  Ensure that drainage of any adjacent land does not affect the wetlands adversely.

– Examine the possibilities of linking wetlands along watercourses into the protective zones; in some circumstances there may be a conservation gain by directing drainage water into them.

– On wet grassland controlled grazing may be necessary to maintain suitable vegetation and conditions for breeding waders and wildfowl.

Old Growth, Dead Trees, Fallen Timber

Trees become more valuable for nature conservation as they become older and eventually become decrepit. Younger woodlands, regardless of species, do not provide a suitable habitat for some flora, such as the lichens which require the attributes of older bark on which to develop. The development of a rich ground flora depends on an adequate supply of light, which is a function of increasing age and stand structure. Great care and thought is necessary before deciding to fell existing old trees. Groups and stands of younger trees should be identified for long-term retention on sites where their conservation value will be high and their expectation of life will be long. Even in areas of high windthrow hazard, sheltered valley bottoms present some opportunities. Management will usually be required.

Dying and dead wood provides one of the greatest resources for fungal and animal species in the forest. Dead trees are also particularly valuable as nest and roost sites for birds and bats.

– Conservation plans should contain provision for retaining some trees through death and complete decay. Trees with bent branches, forks and holes, are particularly suitable because of the number of niches present.

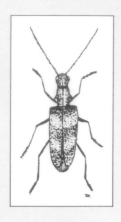

– For these purposes native broadleaves are particularly valuable because they are host to a wide range of species-specific flora and fauna and do not prejudice forest hygiene by harbouring insects injurious to timber-producing conifers.

– Dead wood is most valuable under the canopy where decay is slow.

– Excessive gleaning of firewood can be detrimental to the conservation value.

– For safety's sake do not retain dead trees near roads, paths or other places frequented by the public.

Conservation Benefits of Thinning

A major effect of the world recession of the early 1980s on British woodlands and forests was that thinning was greatly reduced everywhere and not carried out at all in many areas distant from markets. **This has had a detrimental effect, not only on sawlog production but on conservation management, particularly in those areas of high windthrow risk where the opportunity to thin has now passed and the woodlands must remain unthinned to the moment of felling. Fortunately the marketing opportunities now available for small-sized trees means that thinning is again possible.** Within the site specific limits of what can be done without risk of precipitating windblow, opportunities should be taken to:

– adjust the proportions of species present in a mixture;

– remove trees from around watercourses and water-bodies in a manner consistent with good modern practice;

– begin the process of 'feathering' woodland into adjacent open areas;

– encourage the development of a shrub layer of appropriate species throughout the crop;

– encourage the development of an appropriate woodland flora where this is absent and particularly where desirable species will spread as a consequence.

Conversely, in certain circumstances, withholding thinning may be helpful to:

– reduce the spread of invasive species, such as rhododendron;

– conserve micro-habitats dependent upon the still, moist and dark conditions beneath a dense canopy;

– in small areas, discourage disturbance of rare species.

Felling and Restocking

Within a woodland or forest the operation which has the most dramatic effect on wildlife is that of felling. The managerial decisions to be taken about the location, size, configuration and juxtaposition of felling coupes are those, above all, which require detailed information about the ecological processes at work, and through that understanding a view on the conse- quences to wildlife of the operations. There are many areas of Britain where such information is sketchy, and contemporary decisions have to be taken on a theoretical basis. This is, however, a fertile field for current research so that uncertainties are being reduced continuously.

Most contemporary decisions about felling coupes are being taken primarily on the basis of their appearance in the landscape and their practicality for harvesting operations (see *Forest landscape design guidelines*). Fortunately such information as is available about responses from wildlife do not suggest that there is a major conflict between these and conservation objectives. In the broadest sense, small felling coupes are most appropriate in rich, complex, woodland types and large scale coupes are most appropriate in simple, relatively infertile, extensive woodland types, whether they are lowland pinewoods or upland spruce or birch woods.

The moment of restocking is the critical opportunity to reconsider the quantity and distribution of open space, the tree species that are to be replanted or accepted as natural regeneration, and the understorey species it will be appropriate to encourage, whether on a permanent or temporary basis. It is a good discipline for the purposes of future planning to record the decision in a formal way, with a note of the predicted wildlife response.

The conservation value of **natural regeneration** from native tree and shrub species has already been stressed. The value of natural regeneration from other species can only be determined on a site-by-site basis and in the light of objectives. Stands developed from natural regeneration tend to be more diverse than those developed from planting, but there are many other factors to be weighed in the balance.

A large number of **broadleaved tree species have been successfully introduced** to Britain, particularly from Europe, North America and the Far East. Most have no role in woodland or forests as distinct from gardens, parks, etc. A few species have been successful on a large scale and over a long period so that they have become a traditional and treasured part of many landscapes, and major contributors to the hardwood market. Particular examples of such naturalised species are sycamore, and beech where it occurs outside of its natural range (it is native in the southern parts of Britain).

Sycamore may sometimes reduce the nature conservation value of semi-natural woodland because it is such an effective competitor. In these woodlands active management may be required following a careful appraisal of the processes at work. Elsewhere these naturalised species should continue to be planted and encouraged on sites where they grow well and contribute to the landscape or where their nature conservation potential can be realised.

A number of **conifer species** which may not have the highest productive potential do have important attributes in relation to conservation objectives and should be considered for inclusion in planting schemes, whether in mixture or not. Foremost among these species are the larches because their light and deciduous foliage encourages ground flora to develop from an early age. Other species for consideration are those with significant cone crops, such as Norway spruce and Scots pine, which constitute a very important food source for a range of birds and the red squirrel.

Coppicing

The coppicing system reached its zenith a long time ago and has been in decline ever since. **Very few woodlands are now worked on a regular basis for the economic production of coppice wood, but they are of particular value for nature conservation because the coppice system ensures a diversity of habitat within the woodland or forest at any one time.** The small area of traditional market-orientated coppicing is concentrated in the south-east of Britain where it is beneficial to species such as nightingale, garden warbler and dormouse, but, as a system, it can have conservation value right across Britain and should therefore be considered in appropriate circumstances everywhere. Coppicing regimes will be of most wildlife value when:

- rotations are reasonably short so that a large proportion of any woodland is in the early growth period;

- there is a consistent cutting management so that many ages of regrowth are present in the wood at one time;

- the principal species being coppiced is native to the site;

- there are a number of coppice species present and being cut;

- the woodland or forest has open space in the form of rides, roads or clearings;

- the coppice contains some climbers;

- there are 'standard' trees present;

- the coppice stools are old.

Habitat Creation and Enhancement

There will be scope for the creation or enhancement of particular habitats by artificial means. Such projects can bring lasting benefit but they must be complementary to the nature conservation management of the woodland or forest as a whole.

- Assess the expected benefits of projects against their cost; the creation of water-bodies may be particularly expensive but is likely to yield important conservation benefits relatively quickly.

- Make sure that a proposed project will not damage existing values. Flooding a low-lying open area may be a net loss for conservation.

The range of possible projects is extensive. The following have proved to be useful and practical.

- The installation of nest boxes, especially where dead trees are scarce, increases the number of nest sites. Some species nest successfully on the ground yet quickly take to boxes and thus the overall population may not increase significantly. On the other hand populations of species such as barn owl, goldeneye and pied flycatchers, can be increased by providing boxes. Nest boxes may be particularly useful for purposes of research and to attract birds to recreation areas.

- The provision of artificial eyries for osprey or red kite, located in quiet areas of the forest, and simulated crows' nests placed in the zone between moorland and forest edge for merlin and long-eared owl.

- The construction of artificial islands provides nesting sites with more protection against disturbance and predators. Where lake water level fluctuates, floating raft islands are beneficial.

- The installation of boxes for bats is a useful means of finding out which bats are present in the forest and of raising awareness of bats. It is not yet certain how beneficial roosting boxes may be, but they are likely to be useful in those parts of the country where traditional roosting sites in farm buildings and roofs have become scarce.

- Areas of important habitats may be created or extended by making pools and ponds in woodlands which have little or no open water. Expensive dams have rarely been cost-effective on wildlife grounds alone. Pools can often be created as part of road construction works at little extra cost.

- Man-made structures within the forest often provide valuable wildlife sites. Derelict buildings, stabilised and made safe rather than demolished, can be fitted with nesting ledges or boxes for barn owls and kestrels. Ledges provided beneath bridges are valuable nest sites for dippers. Old stone walls often support lichens of great age which can be maintained by providing open space along short sections.

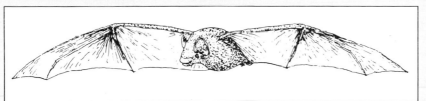

Viewing Wildlife as a Forest Recreation

All the evidence indicates that a principal reason why people visit woodlands and forest is to have the opportunity to experience wildlife. This is a major subject in its own right and it is appropriate here only to touch on a few of the main considerations.

Walks must be designed to lead visitors to where wildlife can be enjoyed without disturbance. Poor planning can lead to significant harm to breeding birds or ground flora. The effect of unrestrained dogs can be devastating, especially to deer populations.

It is often a better strategy to endeavour to increase rare species by management than to try to restrict knowledge of the locations.

It is a mistake to suggest to the generality of visitors that they will have opportunities to experience unusual or rare species, or even relatively common species which are shy or nocturnal.

Conversely there are now excellent precedents for showing even something as rare as a redbacked shrike to hundreds of people at the same time. Ospreys at Loch Garten, peregrines at Symonds Yat and hen harriers at Struie are well-known precedents.

Seek expert specialist advice before embarking on such projects. They can be expensive and must be carefully executed if they are to be successful.

Small hides, located where there is a chance of seeing characteristic animals, can be good value for money. They are a good way of giving people a chance to observe deer. Fallow deer are particularly amenable and quite tame if a sanctuary area is developed.

There are many excellent examples of interpretation of woodland and forest conservation. There are also expensive failures. Seek professional advice.

Sites of Geological and Geomorphological Interest

SSSIs designated for their earth science values will be managed in accordance with a plan agreed with the NCC. Many other non-designated sites of earth science interest have been identified, particularly in upland Britain. Operations which are potentially damaging to these sites are ploughing, draining, road construction and harvesting.

– Survey a new planting site for earth science interest and incorporate appropriate measures into the ploughing and planting designs which will help to safeguard important features. Examples are leaving bold features unplanted, notch planting on moraines, or providing clear views of kames, kettles and eskers. Open ground required for other purposes can often be made to coincide with such sites.

– Take particular care when planning road construction and maintenance work as these operations can have a devastating effect on smaller earth science sites of interest.

– Take opportunities during felling and restocking operations to leave open ground around the most outstanding and least disturbed earth science sites, possibly in conjunction with other conservation objectives. During thinning operations remove any trees which have been planted too close to fragile sites where further tree root growth could have a disrupting effect.

– Where cave SSSIs exist within the same catchment in limestone areas, any forest operation which is likely to have some impact on local hydrological conditions should be discussed with NCC.

Specialist assistance will often be necessary to locate such sites and to propose appropriate management. Prescriptions for sites should be built into conservation plans.

● **Broadleaved Woodland**

A booklet entitled *Guidelines for the management of broadleaved woodland* was published by the Forestry Commission in September 1985 and is essential reading for all engaged in broadleaved forestry. The guidelines are based on the following principles.

- **Woodland which is now broadleaved is expected to remain so.** This means that any areas felled in broadleaved woods will be replaced with crops which are either broadleaved, or which will develop into broadleaved woodland.

- **There is a presumption against clearance of broadleaved woodland for agricultural purposes.** There will have to be very strong reasons for this to be allowed.

- **The present area of broadleaved woodland is expected to increase** by new broadleaved planting on what is now agricultural land, by the natural colonisation of broadleaves on open or waste ground, and by some planting of broadleaves on ground now carrying conifers.

- **Special attention will be given to ancient semi-natural broadleaved woodlands to ensure continuance of their special features.** These woods are irreplaceable and should not be allowed to lose their natural characteristics.

- **Managed woodland is more likely to survive than unmanaged woodland.** For this purpose adequate income from woodland is essential. With good management this can be obtained without detriment to landscape, wildlife or recreational interests, all of which can be better met by healthy, valuable trees than by neglected and moribund growing stock. This is obviously in both the growers' and the national interest, in view of the importance of continuity of supply of the major broadleaved species to the hardwood timber industry.

Native Pinewood

Detailed guidelines for the management of native pinewoods are set out in the Forestry Commission publication *Native pinewoods: grants and guidelines* (1989).

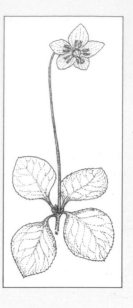

The native pinewoods are among the least modified woodland areas in Britain. They are an irreplaceable reservoir of adapted genetic stock of all the plants and animals of the pinewood. They should be managed so as to:

– maintain and enhance their ecosystems;

– maintain and enhance their aesthetic value;

– enlarge their area, particularly of the smallest pinewoods;

– maintain the genetic integrity of the native population and, so far as practicable, maintain identifiable sub-populations;

– produce utilisable timber.

The management of native pinewoods is a very specialised business. Seek professional advice.

Small Lowland Woods and Shelterbelts

When considered in terms of broad ecological principles, **small woods** may be generally less valuable to wildlife than large woods because they are likely to contain fewer species, smaller populations of species, fewer woodland types and scope for less range of structure and habitat. However, normally set in intensively managed countryside, these small woodlands are often among the few areas of relatively undisturbed land, providing a sanctuary for many species of wildlife and retaining protected natural landforms or important geological sites. Often created within the last 100–200 years, they are predominantly broadleaved or mixed woods, though in some areas of Britain there is a long tradition of conifer shelterbelts and blocks. Many of these small woods were created and are managed for game shooting. Woods designed for pheasants, and which have well-structured edges, shrubby cover within the wood and open feeding areas, are often very good habitats for wildlife. Conversely pheasants stocked at too high densities can have very damaging effects. Excellent practical advice is available from the Game Conservancy and others.

Many **shelterbelts** established as even-aged plantings become draughty and inhospitable as they mature. The key to improving their effectiveness as shelterbelts, and their value to wildlife, is to create a graded edge incorporating shrub species.

Urban and Urban Fringe Woodland

The woods within and surrounding towns and cities tend to have lower nature conservation value than other woodland types because:

- they tend to be well used by man and dogs so that the wildlife interest is dominated by the most resilient species of birds and mammals;

- fragile ground flora tend to be very restricted in occurrence – in some areas air pollution has affected the ability of lichens to colonise these woods;

- due to safety requirements and high public usage, dead wood is very uncommon in these woods.

For these reasons very particular skills are required to maintain and increase conservation value in woodland where the social benefit is high. Seek expert advice, not only for the management of existing woodland but when contemplating the development of new urban woodland.

Conifer High Forest

Most productive high forest in Britain is composed predominantly of conifers, of uniform age over fairly large areas, and with little diversity of tree species. **The aim is to effect a transition from even-aged plantation to well-balanced forest.** The desired result is a woodland or forest which has a sustained yield of the fullest range of habitats. The transition will be effected by a number of strategies, including:

- varying the thinning regime;

- increasing the spread of age classes by some early felling, and especially by delaying felling and by retaining about 1 per cent of the area to be grown on to full physical maturity;

- taking advantage of windthrow when it occurs by phasing the restocking and leaving more open space;

- improving the structure of the forest at the time of felling and restocking – this is a central requirement of good landscape design, which will usually determine the timing, scale and shape of felling coupes;

- introducing or increasing broadleaves on appropriate sites, either by planting or preferably by the natural regeneration of local native species – scattered or clumped broadleaves have a significant conservation value but beware of introducing large-seeded broadleaves if red squirrels are present and grey squirrels are a threat;

- continuously reviewing the amount and distribution of open ground, and how it relates to other open ground, both within and outside the forest – the opportunity is greatest at restocking;

- giving special attention to the transition zones between wooded and open areas;

- widening the range of conifer species, particularly to include some with light canopies, and some with dependable cone crops often in mixture with the principal species;

- in appropriate places, encouraging the development of a shrub layer.

The following notes are intended to act as a summary aide memoire of the points made in more detail in the foregoing paragraphs, and to introduce further points in relation to specific operations.

Planning new planting

- When land is to be planted, opportunities must be taken to make provision for nature conservation from the start.

- Survey the area carefully to establish the presence of communities or habitats of special conservation value and retain these as open ground within the woodland or forest. Make use of soil or land capability maps.

- Ensure that such areas have a sufficient buffer zone so as to protect them from modifications to adjoining sites. This is particularly important in relation to water-bodies and wetlands of all descriptions.

- Take particular account of any semi-natural woodland for its own sake and as a potential seed source. Consider opportunities for enlarging the woodland.

- Lay out the open ground required for roads, water protection zones, service corridors, recreation, deer glades and other purposes. In deciding width, remember to take orientation into account. So far as is practicable, link together these open areas, and look for opportunities to connect with open land in adjoining land use.

Fencing

- Where appropriate, install badger gates and deer leaps.
- In capercaillie areas, consider the use of high visibility fence demarcators to reduce the hazard to flying birds.

Cultivation

- Use the minimum cultivation necessary to achieve the desired ends. For example, do not plough if ripping or scarifying will suffice.

- Ensure that cultivation practice complies with the *Forests and water guidelines*.

Drainage

- Provide sufficient cross drains on ploughed ground to prevent erosive volumes of water accumulating in plough furrows.

- Angle drains at no more than 3 degrees off the contour to prevent erosion.

- Ensure that cross drains are sufficiently deeper than plough furrows to fulfil their function.

- Do not allow drains to enter riparian buffer zones.

- Angle drain ends to reduce water velocity and taper their depth.

- Ensure that drainage practice complies with the *Forests and water guidelines*.

Planting or restocking

- Decide which areas should be left to regenerate naturally, whether immediately or later, for example with birch, and leave these unplanted.

- Plant only light-foliaged broadleaves in riparian zones.

- Where broadleaves are being planted primarily for conservation, use species found naturally in the area.

- Ensure that planting stock is suited to the site conditions, and that plants are properly handled and well planted so that there is a high initial survival and vigorous first-year growth.

Fertilising

– Because of the risk of rapid run-off into watercourses, never apply fertiliser to frozen or snow-covered ground. Plan operations to minimise drift to riparian zones.

Herbicide weeding and cleaning

– Herbicides can be a valuable tool for vegetation management. Choose a method of application which gives the desired level of control with the minimum quantity of active ingredient. Overall application is seldom necessary. Band or spot treatment is usually sufficient.

– Comply with the *Provisional code of practice for the use of pesticides in forestry* (Forestry Commission Occasional Paper 21)

– Where there is a choice of suitable herbicide, choose one with low toxicity and which breaks down quickly in the soil, for example triclopyr, asulam or glyphosate.

– Ensure that the use of herbicides is minimised by timing other establishment operations correctly.

Thinning

– Adjust the proportions of species present in a mixture.

– Remove trees from around watercourses and water-bodies in a manner consistent with good modern practice.

– Begin the process of feathering woodland into adjacent open areas.

– Encourage the development of a shrub layer of appropriate species throughout the crop.

– Encourage the development of an appropriate woodland flora where this is absent and particularly where desirable species will spread as a consequence.

Felling

– Keep brash away from streamsides, open spaces, rides and roadsides by felling trees into the stand near these locations.

– As soon as possible after felling, remove any brash that does enter these areas.

– Keep urea used for stump treatment well away from streams, and do not leave urea on site where it may be tampered with.

– Schedule operations to avoid raptor breeding sites in season.

Extraction

– Plan extraction routes to minimise stream crossings.

– Use temporary culverts on all soft-bottomed or soft-banked stream crossings.

– Never extract along stream beds.

– Use brash mats to reduce soil damage.

– Plan extraction routes to avoid valuable habitat.

- Avoid long downhill extraction routes – use frequent changes of direction. Where there is no alternative, provide cross drains to prevent water flowing down wheel ruts.

- Site refuelling and maintenance areas well away from watercourses.

- Clear up any oil or fuel spills immediately.

- Select firm, dry ground as stacking sites, well away from watercourses.

- Remove temporary culverts from watercourses and pulpwood from drain crossings when operations are complete.

- Repair wheel ruts where these have unavoidably formed on erodible slopes.

Road-building

- Check conservation plans before commencing operations to identify sensitive areas.

- Keep valley bottom roads as far back from streams as possible.

- Protect riparian vegetation in all operations.

- Avoid metalliferous or sulphide-rich material for road construction near watercourses.

- Design roadside drains to avoid direct discharge into natural watercourses. This may mean an additional culvert to bring the upper roadside drain to the lower side as the road approaches stream crossings.

- Seek advice from the local fishery authority about the timing of any in-river work.

- Adhere to the practices set out in the *Forests and water guidelines*.

Forest Protection

- If creating fire traces, use tractor-mounted swipes in preference to bulldozers.

- Ensure that measures adopted to control grey squirrels and rabbits affect only the intended target species.

- Control deer numbers to maintain populations within the carrying capacity of the site (see *The management of red deer in upland forests*, Forestry Commission Bulletin 71).

All operations

- If in doubt, **take advice.**

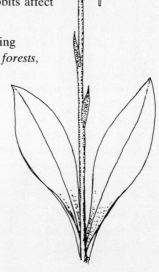

ADVICE ON NATURE CONSERVATION

Nature is diverse and complex. Nobody can expect to be an expert in more than a few fields. A great deal of helpful information and experience is available and should always be sought.

The local office of the Forestry Commission will always be a helpful contact.

– Rangers, keepers and others engaged in the management of wildlife locally, usually have a fund of local knowledge not available elsewhere. This should be used to the full.

– Local naturalists, either individually or through local Nature Conservation Trusts and other societies, are a major source of knowledge. Some are national experts in their field. The Royal Society for the Protection of Birds is very willing to advise on bird conservation.

– Local staff of the Nature Conservancy Council have wide-ranging expertise in nature conservation in their area, including woodland conservation, and are very ready to assist directly and by advising on other sources of information.

– The Forestry Commission Wildlife and Conservation Research Branch specialises in woodland conservation management and makes general advice available through publications on many aspects. Their primary function is research and the dissemination of research findings, and they will be unable to advise on a site-by-site basis. However, they are always willing to discuss major projects or problems.

– The British Trust for Conservation Volunteers, and Scottish Conservation Projects, carry out practical conservation work. These organisations are able to undertake work with a high labour content, unsuitable for mechanisation.

ACKNOWLEDGEMENTS

The text of these guidelines is due substantially to these staff of the Forestry Commission:

– Morton Boyd, Nature Conservation Consultant

– Richard Britton, Wildlife and Conservation Officer

– Graham Gill, Head of Environment Branch

– Rod Leslie, formerly Wildlife and Conservation Officer

– Alastair Rowan, formerly Director Private Forestry and Services Division

– Alistair Scott, Director Private Forestry and Environment Division

The Forestry Commission is grateful to the following organisations who contributed comment and advice:

– Conservation Association of Botanical Societies

– Countryside Commission

– Countryside Commission for Scotland

– Fountain Forestry

– Institute of Chartered Foresters

– Nature Conservancy Council

– Royal Society for Nature Conservation

– Royal Society for the Protection of Birds

– Scottish Wild Land Group

– Scottish Wildlife Trust

– Timber Growers United Kingdom

– Wildlife Link

– World Wide Fund for Nature

Habitat drawings are by Paul Barwick and those of animal and plant species are by John Williams.

Useful Addresses

Forestry Commission
Environment Branch
231 Corstorphine Road
Edinburgh
EH12 7AT

Tel: 031-334 0303

Forestry Commission
Research Division
(Wildlife and Conservation
Research Branch)
Alice Holt Lodge
Wrecclesham
Farnham
Surrey
GU10 4LH

Tel: 0420 22255

Nature Conservancy Council
Northminster House
Peterborough
PE1 1UA

Tel: 0733 40345

Nature Conservancy Council
12 Hope Terrace
Edinburgh
EH9 2AS

Tel: 031-447 4784

Nature Conservancy Council
Plas Penrhos
Ffordd Penrhos
Bungor
Gwynedd
LL57 2LQ

Tel: 0248 370444

**Royal Society for the Protection
of Birds**
The Lodge
Sandy
Bedfordshire
SG19 2DL

Tel: 0767 80551

**Royal Society for the Protection
of Birds**
17 Regent Terrace
Edinburgh
EH7 5BN

Tel: 031-557 3136

**Royal Society for the Protection
of Birds**
Bryn Aderyn
Newtown
Powys
SA16 2AB

Tel: 0686 26678

Farming and Wildlife Trust Ltd
National Agricultural Centre
Stoneleigh
Kenilworth
Warwickshire
CV8 2RX

Tel: 0203 696699

Game Conservancy Trust
Fordingbridge
Hampshire
SP6 1EF

Tel: 0425 52381

**British Trust for Conservation
Volunteers**
36 St Mary's Street
Wallingford
Oxfordshire
OX10 0EU

Tel: 0491 39766

Scottish Conservation Projects
Balallan House
24 Allan Park
Stirling
FK8 2QG

Tel: 0786 79697

Institute of Chartered Foresters
22 Walker Street
Edinburgh
EH3 7HR

Tel: 031 225 2705

Coed Cymru
Frolic Street
Newtown
Powys
SY16 1AP

Tel: 0686 628514

● **Forestry Commission conservancies and forest districts**

**Forestry Commission
Conservancies & Forest Districts**

FORESTRY COMMISSION INFORMATION
Offices

● **EDINBURGH**	Forestry Commission Headquarters
○ York	Conservancy Office
● *Hawick*	Forest District Office
———	Conservancy Boundary
———	Forest District Boundary
BORDER	Forest District Name

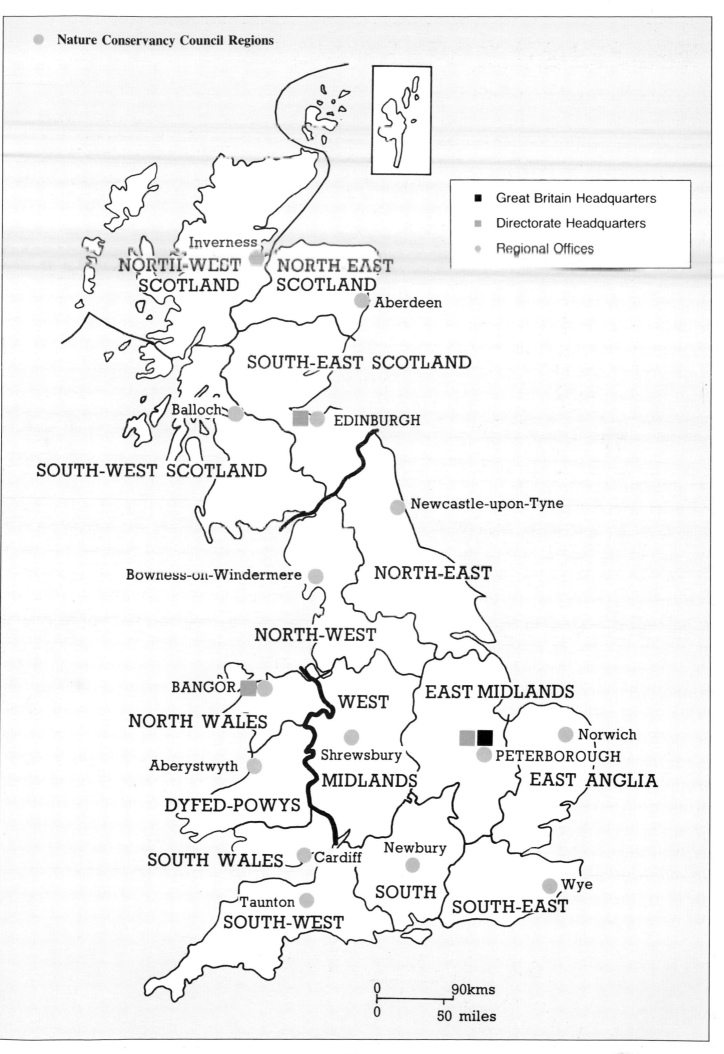

Nature Conservancy Council Regions

Great Britain Headquarters
Directorate Headquarters
Regional Offices

Inverness
NORTH-WEST SCOTLAND
NORTH EAST SCOTLAND
Aberdeen
SOUTH-EAST SCOTLAND
Balloch
EDINBURGH
SOUTH-WEST SCOTLAND
Newcastle-upon-Tyne
NORTH-EAST
Bowness-on-Windermere
NORTH-WEST
BANGOR
WEST
EAST MIDLANDS
NORTH WALES
Norwich
PETERBOROUGH
Aberystwyth
Shrewsbury
EAST ANGLIA
DYFED-POWYS
MIDLANDS
Cardiff
Newbury
SOUTH WALES
SOUTH
Taunton
Wye
SOUTH-WEST
SOUTH-EAST

0   90kms
0   50 miles

LOCAL NATURE CONSERVATION TRUSTS

The following is a list of those trusts in Great Britain associated with the Royal Society for Nature Conservation (RSNC) arranged by countries.

RSNC
The Green
Witham Park
Lincoln
LN5 7JR

Tel: 0522 544400

Trusts in England

Avon Wildlife Trust
The Old Police Station
32 Jacob's Wells Road
Bristol
BS8 1DR

Tel: 0272 268018/265490

Bedfordshire and Huntingdonshire Wildlife Trust
Priory Country Park
Barkers Lane
Bedford
MK41 8SH

Tel: 0234 64213

Berkshire, Buckinghamshire and Oxon Naturalists' Trust (BBONT)
3 Church Cowley Road
Rose Hill
Oxford
OX4 3JR

Tel: 0865 775476

Urban Wildlife Group (Birmingham) (UWG)
Unit 213
Jubilee Trade Centre
130 Pershore Street
Birmingham
B5 6ND

Tel: 021-666 7474

Cambridgeshire Wildlife Trust
5 Fulbourn Manor
Manor Walk
Fulbourn
Cambridge
CB1 5BN

Tel: 0223 880788

Cheshire Conservation Trust
Marbury Country Park
Northwich
Cheshire
CW9 0AT

Tel: 0606 781868

Cleveland Wildlife Trust
The Old Town Hall
Mandale Road
Thornaby
Cleveland
TS17 6AW

Tel: 0642 608405

Cornwall Trust for Nature Conservation
Five Acres
Allet
Truro
Cornwall
TR4 9DJ

Tel: 0872 73939

Cumbria Wildlife Trust
Church Street
Ambleside
Cumbria
LA22 0BU

Tel: 0966 32476

Derbyshire Wildlife Trust
Elvaston Castle Country Park
Derby
DE7 3EP

Tel: 0332 756610

Devon Wildlife Trust
35 New Bridge Street
Exeter
Devon
EX3 4AH

Tel: 0392 79244

**Dorset Trust for Nature
Conservation**
39 Christchurch Road
Bournemouth
Dorset
BH1 3NS

Tel: 0202 24241

Durham Wildlife Trust
52 Old Elvet
Durham
DH1 3HN

Tel: 091-386 9797

Essex Naturalists' Trust
Fingringhoe Wick Nature Reserve
Fingringhoe
Colchester
Essex
CO5 7DN

Tel: 0206 28678

**Gloucestershire Trust for Nature
Conservation**
Church House
Standish
Stonehouse
Glos
GL10 3EU

Tel: 045 382 2761

**Hampshire and Isle of Wight
Naturalists' Trust**
71 The Hundred
Romsey
Hants
SO51 8BZ

Tel: 0794 513786

Herefordshire Nature Trust
Community House
25 Castle Street
Hereford
HR1 2NW

Tel: 0432 356872

**Hertfordshire and Middlesex
Wildlife Trust**
Grebe House
St Michael's Street
St Albans
Herts
AL3 4SN

Tel: 0727 58901

**Kent Trust for Nature
Conservation**
The Annexe
1a Bower Mount Road
Maidstone
Kent
ME16 8AX

Tel: 0622 53017/59017

**Lancashire Trust for Nature
Conservation**
The Pavilion
Cuerden Park Wildlife Centre
Shady Lane
Bamber Bridge
Preston
Lancs
PR5 6AU

Tel: 0772 324129

**Leicestershire and Rutland Trust
for Nature Conservation**
1 West Street
Leicester
LE1 6UU

Tel: 0533 553904

**Lincolnshire and South
Humberside Trust for Nature
Conservation**
The Manor House
Alford
Lincs
LN13 9DL

Tel: 052 12 3468

London Wildlife Trust
80 York Way
London
N1 9AG

Tel: 01-278 6612/3

Norfolk Naturalists' Trust
72 Cathedral Close
Norwich
Norfolk
NR1 4DF

Tel: 0603 625540

Northants Wildlife Trust
Lings House
Billing Lings
Northampton
NN3 4BE

Tel: 0604 405285

Northumberland Wildlife Trust
Hancock Museum
Barras Bridge
Newcastle-upon-Tyne
NE2 4PT

Tel: 091-232 0038

Nottinghamshire Wildlife Trust
310 Sneinton Dale
Nottingham
NG3 7DN

Tel: 0602 588242

Shropshire Wildlife Trust
St George's Primary School
Frankwell
Shrewsbury
Shropshire
SY3 8JP

Tel: 0743 241691

**Somerset Trust for Nature
Conservation**
Fyne Court
Broomfield
Bridgwater
Somerset
TA5 2EQ

Tel: 0823 451587/8

**Staffordshire Nature Conservation
Trust**
Coutts House
Sandon
Staffordshire
ST18 0DN

Tel: 08897 534

Suffolk Wildlife Trust
Park Cottage
Saxmundham
Suffolk
IP17 1DQ

Tel: 0728 603765

Surrey Wildlife Trust
The Old School
School Lane
Pirbright
Woking
Surrey
GU24 0JN

Tel: 0483 797575

Sussex Wildlife Trust
Woods Mill
Shoreham Road
Henfield
West Sussex
BN5 9SD

Tel: 0273 492630

**Warwickshire Nature
Conservation Trust (WARNACT)**
Montague Road
Warwick
CV34 5LW

Tel: 0926 496848

**Wiltshire Trust for Nature
Conservation**
19 High Street
Devizes
Wiltshire
SN10 1AT

Tel: 0380 5670

**Worcestershire Nature
Conservation Trust**
Hanbury Road
Droitwich
Worcestershire
WR9 7DU

Tel: 0905 773031

Yorkshire Wildlife Trust
10 Toft Green
York
YO1 1JT

Tel: 0904 659570

Trusts in Wales

Brecknock Wildlife Trust
Lion House
7 Lion Street
Brecon
Powys
LD3 7AY

Tel: 0874 5708

Dyfed Wildlife Trust
7 Market Street
Haverfordwest
Dyfed
3A61 1NT

Tel: 0437 5462

Glamorgan Wildlife Trust
Nature Centre
Fountain Road
Tondu
Mid Glamorgan
CF32 0EH

Tel: 0656 724100

Gwent Wildlife Trust
16 White Swan Court
Church Street
Monmouth
Gwent
NP5 3BR

Tel: 0600 5501

Montgomeryshire Wildlife Trust
8 Severn Square
Newtown
Powys
SY16 2AG

Tel: 0686 624751

North Wales Wildlife Trust
376 High Street
Bangor
Gwynedd
LL57 1YE

Tel: 0248 351541

Radnorshire Wildlife Trust
1 Gwalia Annexe
Ithon Road
Llandrindod Wells
Powys
LD1 6AS

Tel: 0597 3298

Trust in Scotland

Scottish Wildlife Trust (SWT)
25 Johnston Terrace
Edinburgh
EH1 2NH

Tel: 031-226 4602

REFERENCES AND FURTHER READING

- **Forestry Commission Publications**

Policy, guidelines and grants

Guidelines for the management of broadleaved woodland (1985)

Policy Paper 4: *The Forestry Commission and conservation* (1986)

Woodland grant scheme (1988)

Farm woodland scheme (1988)

Forests and water guidelines (1988)

Environmental assessment of afforestation projects (1988)

Forest landscape design guidelines (1989)

Native pinewoods: grants and guidelines (1989)

Conservation

Wildlife rangers' handbook (1985)

Bulletin 62: *Silviculture of broadleaved woodland* (1984)

Bulletin 71: *The management of red deer in upland forests* (1987)

Bulletin 78: *Natural regeneration of broadleaves* (1988)

Bulletin 81: *Goshawks: their status, requirements and management* (1989)

Leaflet 86: *Glades for deer control in upland forests* (1986)

Leaflet 88: *Use of broadleaved species in upland forests* (1986)

Research Information Note 126: *Enhancement of lowland forest ridesides and roadsides to benefit wild plants and butterflies* (1987)

Research Information Note 153: *Hopper modification for grey squirrel control* (1989)

Research Information Note 157: *Effects of broadleaved trees on birds of conifer plantations in North Wales — Report of joint RSPB/FC study 1984* (1989)

Research Information Note 180: *Grey squirrel damage control with warfarin* (1990)

There is also a wide range of specific wildlife publications covering many of the more important forest fauna and flora. They are listed in the Forestry Commission's *Catalogue of publications* available free on request from:

Forestry Commission Publications,
Alice Holt Lodge,
Wrecclesham, Farnham,
Surrey GU10 4LH

● Other Publications

Nature Conservancy Council

A nature conservation review, Vols. 1 and 2 (1977)

Nature conservation and afforestation in Britain (1986)

Site management plans for nature conservation: a working guide (1988)

Guidelines for selection of biological SSSIs (1989)

The NCC also publishes a series of short leaflets on particular habitats and species groups. These provide a clear and brief introduction to their subjects and may be particularly useful when dealing with unfamiliar habitats.

Royal Society for the Protection of Birds

Birds and broadleaves handbook (1985)

Small woodlands and birds (1987)

New farm woods and birds (1988)

Broadleaved woodland management and birds (1989)

Birds and coppice (1989)

Woodpeckers and dead wood (1989)

Institute of Terrestrial Ecology

Trees and wildlife in the Scottish uplands, Symposium No. 17 (1986)

Pasture woodlands in lowland Britain (1986)

Timber Growers United Kingdom

The forestry and woodland code (1985)

Institute of Chartered Foresters

Wildlife management in forests (1988)

Other sources

G. F. Peterken	*Woodland conservation and management* (1981). Chapman and Hall, London.
Oliver Rackham	*Ancient woodland: its history, vegetation and uses in England* (1980). Edward Arnold, London.
Oliver Rackham	*The history of the countryside* (1986). J.M. Dent and Sons, London.
Oliver Rackham	*Trees and woodland in the British landscape,* 2nd edtn (1990). J.M. Dent and Sons, London.

*Reproduced by kind permission from the Tree Council's magazine *Tree news*, September 1989
Copies of *Tree news* are available free on request from: The Tree Council, 35 Belgrave Square, London, SW1X 8NQ. Tel: 071 235 8854.
The consent of the authors and of the Nature Conservancy Council is also gratefully acknowledged.

NATIVE TREES AND SHRUBS FOR WILDLIFE

by Rob Soutar and George Peterken

Native tree and shrub species are not only valuable components of the natural heritage of the United Kingdom, they also provide much of the native wildlife with its natural habitats. Some native tree and shrub species are commonly associated with a prodigious diversity and biomass of wildlife, whilst other less bountiful species provide habitat for specialised fauna and flora. Thus for example, the native oaks support more insects than do any other British trees, but only the native buckthorns support the larvae of the brimstone butterfly. Whatever the abundance or rarity of their associated wildlife, tree and shrub species are usually of highest value to nature conservation when they grow in places where they would occur naturally in the absence of human disturbance or assistance through the ages.

Location of numbered zones used in table

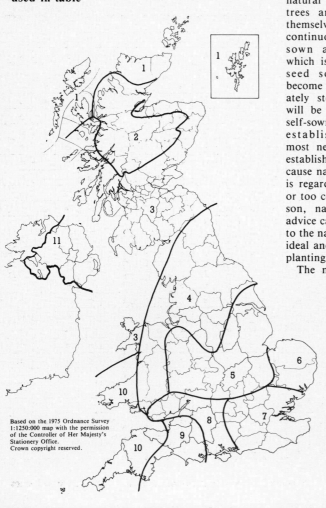

Based on the 1975 Ordnance Survey 1:1250:000 map with the permission of the Controller of Her Majesty's Stationery Office.
Crown copyright reserved.

Indigenous tree and shrub species are not necessarily native everywhere in the U.K. Beech for example, is native in southern England and south-east Wales because it occupied these areas naturally. It is not native in northern Britain, although it is common enough as a planted tree, and as self-sown individuals springing from seed produced ultimately by a planted tree. Conversely, Scots pine was once native in England and Wales but was naturally replaced by broadleaved species, and is now regarded as native only in the Scottish Highlands. Regeneration of pine in lowland Britain is always ultimately associated with planted trees.

From the nature conservation point of view, the ideal way to create new woodlands is to encourage natural regeneration from trees and shrubs which themselves spring from a continuous line of self-sown ancestors. Land which is close to a good seed source may well become rapidly and adequately stocked, and there will be some sites where self-sown trees are already established. However, most new woodlands are established by planting because natural regeneration is regarded as impractical or too costly. For this reason, nature conservation advice cannot be restricted to the natural regeneration ideal and must encompass planting.

The map on this page shows eleven zones in which different species are recommended for use in afforestation and amenity planting programmes. The boundaries reflect the broad pattern of natural distribution, but are not precise. They most closely follow the presumed natural distributions of Scots pine, small-leaved lime, bird cherry, hornbeam and beech.

The natural geographical limits of native species are complex and seldom known with precision. In the compilation of lists of species suitable for each zone, many details of distribution have been necessarily ignored in order to concentrate on the broad pattern. Most species match tolerably well with their particular combination of zones; the most conspicuous misfit amongst the larger trees is probably black poplar. Some guidance on the site requirements of each species is also given. Our aim is to encourage the successful establishment of British species in regions and on soils where they are indigenous, so that the character and composition of local and regional treescapes, and their associated wildlife, are maintained. The maps and tables are not suitable for use in the management of ancient and semi-natural woodlands, where more detailed information is needed.

When creating new woodlands, it is best to plant the same native species that occur in nearby ancient and semi-natural woodland. It will usually be most appropriate to encourage common and already widespread species rather than rarer ones. The needs of the latter are often poorly understood. If used they may well be planted on sites or soils where they would not naturally occur or thrive; such a result could be expensive and of little value to nature conservation.

Planting of native trees and shrubs can damage nature conservation interests, even if they are planted in the appropriate zones. This applies particularly to species with local forms, and to those whose distributions are of scientific interest. The problem with planting, even in the correct zone, is that scientific information, including local genetic variety, may be lost or confused. For this reason, it is recommended that certain species in selected zones should only be planted if stock of local origin is used, and if a record is made of the planting. Seed should be collected from semi-natural stands no further away than, say, 10 miles from where the stock is to be planted.

Ideally, all planting of native species should be restricted to stock of local origin.

Rob Soutar and Dr George Peterken are members of the Chief Scientist Directorate of the Nature Conservancy Council. The data for Northern Ireland in the species table was provided by the Department of the Environment for Northern Ireland.

NATIVE SPECIES TO ENCOURAGE IN THE NUMBERED ZONES

LARGE AND MEDIUM SIZED TREES		Zones											Soils					
		1	2	3	4	5	6	7	8	9	10	11	a	b	c	d	e	f
alder, black	Alnus glutinosa	•	•	•	•	•	•	•	•	•	•	L	•				•	
apple, crab	Malus sylvestris spp sylvestris			•	•	•	•	•	•	•	•	L		•	•		•	
ash	Fraxinus excelsior	•	•	•	•	•	•	•	•	•	•	L	•	•	•		•	•
aspen	Populus tremula	•	•	•								L		•		•	•	•
aspen	Populus tremula				•	•	•	•	•	•	•				•		•	
beech	Fagus sylvatica						•	•	•					•		•	•	•
birch, downy	Betula pubescens	•	•	•	•	•	•	•	•	•	•	L	•	•	•	•	•	•
birch, silver	Betula pendula	•	•	•	•	•	•	•	•	•	•	L		•		•	•	•
cherry, bird	Prunus padus	•	•	•	•	L						L	•				•	
cherry, gean	Prunus avium			•	•	•	•	•	•	•	•	L		•			•	
elm, wych	Ulmus glabra	•	•	•	•	•	•	•	•	•	•	L			•		•	•
hornbeam	Carpinus betulus						•	•							•	•	•	
lime, small-leaved	Tilia cordata				L									•			•	
lime, small-leaved	Tilia cordata					L	L	L	L	L				•	•	•	•	
lime, large-leaved	Tilia platyphyllos				L	L		L							•		•	
maple, field	Acer campestre				L	•	•	•	•	•	•			•	•		•	
oak, common	Quercus robur		•	•	•	•	•	•	•	•	•	L	•		•	•	•	
oak, sessile	Quercus petraea		•	•	•	L	L	L	L	L	•	L		•		•	•	
pine, Scots	Pinus sylvestris		L											•		•	•	
poplar, black	Populus nigra var betulifolia					L	L	L	L	L				•			•	
poplar, grey	Populus canescens						•	•	•	•				•			•	
rowan	Sorbus aucuparia	•	•	•	•	•	•	•	•	•	•	L		•		•		•
service-tree	Sorbus torminalis					L	L	L	L	L	L				•	•	•	
whitebeam	Sorbus aria sensu lato		L		L				L			L		•			•	•
whitebeam	Sorbus aria sensu lato							L						•			•	•
willow, crack	Salix fragilis			•	•	•	•	•	•	•	•		•				•	•
willow, goat	Salix caprea	•	•	•	•	•	•	•	•	•	•	L	•		•		•	•
willow, white	Salix alba			•	•	•	•	•	•	•	•	L	•				•	•
yew	Taxus baccata				L		L	L						•			•	

SMALL TREES AND SHRUBS		Zones											Soils					
		1	2	3	4	5	6	7	8	9	10	11	a	b	c	d	e	f
blackthorn	Prunus spinosa	•	•	•	•	•	•	•	•	•	•	L	•	•			•	
box	Buxus sempervirens							L	L					•			•	
broom	Cytisus scoparius	•	•	•	•	•	•	•	•	•	•	L		•			•	•
buckthorn, alder	Frangula alnus				•	•	•	•	•	•			•			•	•	
buckthorn, purging	Rhamnus catharticus				•	•	•	•	•						•		•	
butcher's broom	Ruscus aculeatus							•	•							•	•	
dogwood	Cornus sanguinea				L	•	•	•	•	•				•	•		•	
elder	Sambucus nigra		•	•	•	•	•	•	•	•	•	L		•	•		•	
gorse	Ulex europaeus	•	•	•	•	•	•	•	•	•	•	L		•		•	•	•
guelder-rose	Viburnum opulus	•	•	•	•	•	•	•	•	•	•	L	•				•	
hawthorn, common	Crataegus monogyna	•	•	•	•	•	•	•	•	•	•	L		•	•		•	
hawthorn, Midland	Crataegus laevigata					L	L	L	L						•		•	
hazel	Corylus avellana	•	•	•	•	•	•	•	•	•	•	L		•	•		•	
holly	Ilex aquifolium	•	•	•	•	•	•	•	•	•	•	L		•		•	•	
juniper	Juniperus communis	L	L	L	L			L	L					•		•	•	•
privet	Ligustrum vulgare				•	•	•	•	•	•				•	•		•	
rose, dog	Rosa canina	•	•	•	•	•	•	•	•	•	•	L		•	•		•	
rose, field	Rosa arvensis				•	•	•	•	•	•					•		•	
spindle	Euonymus europaeus				•	•	•	•	•	•	•	L			•		•	
spurge-laurel	Daphne laureola				•	•	•	•	•					•	•		•	
wayfaring-tree	Viburnum lantana					•		•	•	•				•	•		•	
willow, almond	Salix triandra				•	•	•	•	•	•			•				•	
willow, bay	Salix pentandra			•	•							L	•				•	
willow, eared	Salix aurita	•	•	•	•	•	•	•	•	•	•	L	•			•	•	
willow, grey	Salix cinerea	•	•	•	•	•	•	•	•	•	•	L	•			•	•	
willow, osier	Salix viminalis	•	•	•	•	•	•	•	•	•			•				•	
willow, purple	Salix purpurea			•	•	•	•	•	•	•	•	L	•				•	•

SOILS: a = wet sites   b = light, dry soils   c = heavy soils   d = acid   e = neutral or alkaline   f = exposed sites
L = only stock of local origin should be used
These lists are not intended for use in the management of ancient and semi-natural woodlands.

NOTES

NOTES

Printed in the UK for HMSO
Dd. 294468 3/93 C35 531/3 12521